# MERLIN'S METEORITE

RADAR IMAGE OF
MERLIN'S METEORITE.

## THE STORY OF THE ILKLEY MOOR METEORITE.

### BY GORDON T. HOLMES.

## MILLENNIUM EDITION.

## SASRG PRESS

## ACKNOWLEDGEMENTS:

A BIG THANK YOU TO ALL THE GOOD PEOPLE WHO MAY HAVE CONTRIBUTED THEIR KNOWLEDGE, GUIDANCE AND GENERAL HELP TOWARDS THE PUBLICATION OF THIS BOOK.

Dedicated to my Mother, Two Brothers (inc One Family) and the Cat.

TWITCHY III

British Library Cataloguing in Publication Data. A catalogue record for this book is available from the British Library.

## MERLIN'S METEORITE.
The story of the Ilkley Moor Meteorite.

First published in 1999 by  SASRG PRESS

## ISBN   0 9524804 2 5

## PREFACE.

In this Age of Information, the warp drive is provided for by the Media and Internet Engines. With the twilight of the *'Nano 90s'* passing and the expectant century of the *'Transcendental 2,000s'* approaching, the future has just arrived. The Era of Solutions is upon us, for we must control the forces correctly, if we are all to benefit. I do not speak only of the human race or the rest of the living entity in existent on this planet, but the whole control system we call Earth.

There is something out there beyond the Earth's orbital path around the Sun. It is just waiting to destroy our little shared community. It will come one day, that we can be certain of. Our little Blue Oasis in the Blackness of Infinity is on borrowed time. No one yet knows when it will arrive, but the consequences because of it, may be so great that it is probably beyond our ability to prevent or avoid it. That which I speak of, is the *'Doomsday Rock'*, a Meteorite over 5km across that will impact the planet and wipe out most of life on Earth.

Now some will say it will never happen, but the truth is, it has already occurred in our historical past. One such event 65 million years ago is believed to have wiped out 99% of all Dinosaurs. Our only survivor, within the British Isle, might be the *'Kelpie'*, better known to most of us as The Lochness Monster or *'Nessie'*.

With luck, the threat from space may be millions of years in the future, Mankind should have populated Mars, the Moon and the odd Asteroid, so as a Species we should survive. This is the main reason why Mankind must advance into Space, is to spread out and there by prevent complete extinction, due to one worldwide disaster of a planet's civilization.

Scientist have began to realise the threat from space is now considered greater than was previously thought fifteen years ago. If is often said we should understand our enemy, thus studying the Science of Meteorites would be to study ones futuristic potential enemy. Once you begin to research into these building blocks of the early forming Solar System, you realise that many different topics need to be considered for study. Geology, Orbital Mechanics, Statistics, Astronomy: - both Optical and Radio, History and Geography are just a few topics that are called upon when delving into Meteorites.

My expedition on Ilkley Moor to search for Meteorites may be very optimistic. However, halfway into the 10-week part-time moorland adventure I did uncover a very unusual stone with all the characteristics of a Meteorite. The feeling was so satisfying that it inspired me to write a documentary about the event and to publish a small novel, which are both included in this book. Like most things in life, one is never able to predict the overall outcome due to an event; this is what makes our experiences so stimulating.

If a few readers become more interested in Meteorites as a result of this book, then that is reward enough and who knows one of you may be so lucky as to find one. Then you will experience something very special!

*'To find that which has never been seen before'.*

**4**

# INTRODUCTION.

It was a realisation that began to develop after the events of 1994 and the observations of the *Shoemaker-Levy 9 Comet.* Over twenty-three fragments from the original comet were monitored by Earth based telescopes and spacecraft for several months. Eventually, the bits of comet ended their journey when they bombarding the planet Jupiter. A whole new concept was born, which suggested that Meteorites might also impact the Earth at a higher rate than was traditionally thought possible by Astronomers only ten years ago.

Due to the events of 1994, plus a number of recent televised scientific documentaries and discussions with friends, I gradually began to consider a new pastime. It was to search locally, for Meteorites. All the indications seemed to suggest that anyone prepared to spend hours searching for these objects from Space, may be lucky enough to discover an odd specimen or two. Previously, finding Meteorites was considered an extremely rare pastime, especially when you consider that only about twenty-two examples have been found in this country. In certain areas of the World, it is possible to find many Meteorites within a small area. This is due to the type of landscape and conditions that prevail there. Antarctica and the Australian Outback are two very special areas where many such items have been found.

This Documentary/Novel occurred as a result of an object, which was found halfway into a 10-week part-time search over the moors of Ilkley during the Summer of 1999. The stone's colour, texture and density had all the characteristics of a Meteorite. The experience of finding a potential meteorite was so stimulating it inspired me to write and publish this book. There are no clues here to the eventual outcome regarding the stone or part metal object. You will need to read the whole text to find if the outcome was the genuine article based on expert Physical and Chemical Analysis.

*'Merlin's Meteorite'* ------------------------- *Novel.*

*'The Story of the Ilkley Moor Meteorite'* ---- *Documentary.*

*Hope you enjoy the story as much as the satisfaction I experienced from writing it and who knows, one day Ilkley may be visited by an/another extra-terrestrial object. With a bit of luck, someone may decide to produce a film based on this book, hope I live to see it!*   *Good Reading.*

## MERLIN'S OR KING ARTHUR'S NORTHERN HEADQUARTERS.

If King Arthur had been born within the White Rose County of Yorkshire, instead of picking York, my guess is he would have made his 'Camelot' near Ilkley. Why, you may ask?

The Moorlands around Ilkley, are a superb mystical setting for any story of Merlin, Magic and Myth. Olicana, the Roman name for Ilkley, was pre-inhabited by Bronze, Neolithic and later, Iron Age peoples. The Pre-historic settlers even left over 600 examples of, as yet, undecoded stone carvings, in the form of Cup & Ring Stones. These strange patterns in rock are believed to be over 4,000 years old. Those Organized Romans even had package road-tours through the area, on-route to the North or West. Ilkley then, was a Transport Service Area for trade, treasures and conquest. Every Merlin or Camelot, must have a Magical Well and Ilkley's representative, comes in the form of the White Wells, situated on the Northern slope between the town and the Moors.

In recent times, a Great Poet or Song Writer, dependent on your own views, wrote a Famous Ballad about Ilkley Moor, which most Kids in the Country will know of as: - *On Ilkley Moor Baht 'at.*

The best known of all the Cup & Ring Stones found on Ilkley Moor is the *Swastika Rock.* According to historical sources, it is a primitive symbol for fire. If this is true, it supports my theory regarding early Cup & Ring Stones were used as FirePlaces. - *(2,000BC - A Cup & Ring Stone Trek. ISBN 09524804 3 3)*

## THE STORY OF THE ILKLEY MOOR METEORITE.

### SUMMER 1999

The find of a Meteorite in the UK is long over due, although, there was a recent case, based on a story in the tabloids, stating that an expert had found a specimen on the ground. I cannot say if this has been confirmed, at this time. If masses of Geology students or other similar experts roamed the landscape, surely several examples would begin to turn up. The biggest problem is the knowing, if you have found one or not.

If there are any Fossils and/or Gem Fairs near you, inquire if there are any stands that sell Meteorites and Tektites. My locals Gem Fairs include: - Ilkley, Harrogate and York Race Course. Further away, there are single events in the Lake District and Peak District. Overall, there are about thirty Gem Fairs around Britain. If you have access to the Network, then try your Search Engine with terms such as: - meteorites UK

Unfortunately, the demand in the UK is not that great. Where would you expect the top meteor-hunters to come from? The United States is the number one Meteorite-Hot-Spot. This is obvious, when you access the US Web-Sites. In this first year that I have become interested in Meteorites, I have enjoyed the hobby.

# A POSSIBLE CREATION OF LIFE, BUT NOT HAS WE KNOW IT.

Over millions of years, Comets from the far reaches of the young solar system rained down upon the cooling molten Earth. As the Oceans formed, great masses of cosmic material plunged into the hot Temperature Sea. These cosmic masses had a high percentage of water, clay-like mud with virtually no metal present. Originally, this mixture of frozen solid chemicals came from the processes that formed the moon Triton. Neptune is the parent planet of this frozen-solid world, near to the outer edge of our family of planets.

Sinking slowly down through an increasing pressure of seawater, the solid mass began to turn into extremely fine grains of different constituents, In time, some of this space-slime merged into the circulating plumes of super-heated water thermals. These thermals were formed due to hot underwater volcanic vents. Unlike today, most areas of the sea floor were covered with these super-steam sources of energy which eventually began to form the building block-molecules necessary for life.

Thanks to rare earth elements, present in the impacting leftovers from the Comets, an essential mixing developed into a solution with earth based chemistry. Highly complex chains of molecules began to form, creating the first bio-duplication systems under the sea. These early evolutionary reactions happened very quickly in the formation of the planet, today there is no evidence remaining of this primitive pro-life fermentation. In addition to this semi-living-mould, microscopic crystals from the Earth's Geology began to be attracted to crystals from Triton's Geology. The outcome was a cluster of three crystals producing a minute emf (voltage) that acted as if magnetized, thus attracting the semi-living-mould to coat the crystals surface. Within the mould, tiny oxidizing iron particles heated up the broth locally; this now extinct process produced the first true organic matter on Earth. Life was born on the third planet out from the Sun.

Half a billion years later, the low lands were infested with this alpha-life-form. In time, these first stage-living entities acquired the ability to survive high levels of solar radiation. This would prove useful for future space travel.

The earth entered successive periods of Ice Ages, causing sea levels to rise and fall continuously. New variations of life became established on land. During the next heavy bombardment of Meteorites through the methane-rich-atmosphere, several forms of life were blasted out into space, protected by a molten outer covering that formed during the earlier impact. Some of these bio-parcels headed in the direction of the outer planets. Eventually, a few entering a decaying orbit towards the planet Mars.

Over three billion years ago, Mars was a hot planet with an atmosphere. As these Earth rocks fell, their inner living contents spilt open onto the Martian surface. The Earthlings had arrived to colonize Mars, at a primitive evolutionary level. After many millions of years of evolution, unbelievable, Meteorites would strike Mars and send back the Earthlings, now Martians, back to Earth. I hope you can follow all this. Twelve thousand years ago, the odd pieces crashed landed in Antarctica, where in recent times they were discovered. After examination, small fossil-like structures were visible which led NASA, the American Space Agency, to claim that here was evidence of life from Mars. At present, the debate still rages on, whether it was life or just some unusual chemical reaction. What a remarkable journey, after billions of years this primitive life, produced higher life-forms now capable of understanding many aspects of the Universe that we are a tiny part of.

7

# IT LOOKS AND FEELS LIKE A METEORITE, BUT IS IT ONE?

Halfway into my search, during the summer of 1999, for a Meteorite across Ilkley Moor, I found something very promising on a steep muddy slope. This mud bank had been recently eroded by heavy rains, so I was probably the first person to see this half buried rock for some time. It appeared to be a Meteorite, consisting of a dark, glassy appearance, with a mass about three times that of a normal terrestrial rock. There was even meteorite-like ablations covering the outer surface. 'Ablations' are dimple-like-recesses that are a strong characteristic, often found on the surface of Meteorites.

Although this mysterious stone did not have a strong magnet attraction, it does however, possess a low-level magnetic field, suggesting some iron is present within it.

PHOTOGRAPH OF THE STONE
I FOUND ON ILKLEY MOOR.

THE STONE FROM ANOTHER ANGLE.

Another strong Meteorite indicator is the overall outer geometrical shape of the stone, consisting of a roughly tapered cylindrical cone with a slight convex bottom, very typical of an object's melted shape has it passes through the Earth's Atmosphere. In fact, the shape is very similar to the design of the Mercury Space Capsules flown by American Astronauts in the early 1960s.

Everything about the stone gave you a positive impression that, here was a rock from space. Even with all the positive feedback, I still had my doubts based purely on the fact that, surely I could not be so lucky as to find a Meteorite so quickly after a five-week part-time search.

There was only one thing for it; I would have to contact the experts for their opinion.

Since I am employed, has a Computer/Electronics Technician at the University of Bradford, in the Department of Archaeological Sciences, I have access to the Internet. After some research, I discovered that all Meteorites found in this country should be sent to the Natural History Museum in London for Examination. Using the Email system, I described my find and was advised to send a sample, the size of a walnut.

The thought of breaking up the stone was too much to bear, so I decided to approach other persons in the know. After discussing the find to an expert in Ancient Metallurgy, within the department, Dr Gerry McDonnell explained that there was a Departmental Instrument capable of defining any mineral content present in the rock. Known as 'XRF', the instrument produces a graph of the mineral signatures due to X-RAY waves bombarding the object.

# A VISIT TO THE VAULTS OF LEEDS CITY MUSEUM, MYSTERY SOLVED?

After explaining the find to the Curate of the Leeds City Museum over the telephone, I was invited to bring the rock along for closer examination. So the Day of Judgement had arrived, today the outcome to the mystery should be solved. This little specimen had so concentrated my activities for the past few weeks. The place of examination was not at the main Museum building, but at the large storerooms. This is sited at the other side of Leeds, near the Railway Station. From the storeroom offices, you have a commanding view of the Multi-Level Car Parks. On arrival, I was met by the Curate, a Staff member who was near to retirement and a young Lady that was on placement here for a couple of weeks. After the polite introductions, the possible space rock was handed over for imminent analysis: -

Encouragingly, after what seemed a lifetime examined under a magnifying glass, the first comment made was, "*Umm, it does look like a Meteorite*".

Gosh, my heartbeat had just increased 30 thuds a minute. Not that the thought of finding a possible 5,000 pounds-worth of stone, had occurred to me, should this be the genuine object. Even if the stone had originated in Space, it is doubtful that I would have wanted to sell it.

The next test required a dark room to examine the stone under Fluorescent/UV Light. You will never guess the place we found to conduct this test, yes the *Ladies Loo*. So for the sake of Science, three of us crammed into the smallest *loo* I have ever seen. There was not enough room to fit a Cat's Whisker. Please note, this was my first and only likely visit to the Ladies. Should any reader at this point, wish to ask any Questions. The answer is NO, whatever the question may be! The result of this test proved negative since no strange glow radiated off the thing.

The third test, the one that should or could clinch it, was the *Acid Test*.

A small drop of Diluted Acid was placed on the stone. It began to fizz,"Ow No"; even I knew that was a bad sign. My Meteorite had just become Limestone in everything, but looks.

Test Four; was the high powered Microscopic Examination. On the surface of this now cheap, good for nothing lump of no-good critter, appeared what looked to be, a few small fossils. Although we were never certain, there appeared to be fossil-like creatures embedded in the stone.

After further reference to books and charts, it was the Curator's opinion that the stone was probably a Basin-Limestone, about 350-380 million years old. However, the geology of Ilkley Moor does not include Limestone and since the nearest location for such rocks of this type, is ancient marine silt found in the Yorkshire Dales, something must have transported it to Whafedale. That mechanism was probably a Glacier from the Last Ice Age, over 12 thousand years ago. In addition, since Basin-Limestone's are normally found deep underground, this little stone must have had a fascinating journey. Another possibility for this now probable piece of Limestone is, it may have been used in Victorian times to produce quicklime for walls, or used in some other form/process. Finally, the suggestion was made that, although the tests were supportive of the theory, that this little stone is limestone. It is still not 100% certain. No doubt, splitting open the stone should confirm the issue, but I still cannot make that decision. In a way, this innocent piece of moorland mystery has been a friend now for a few months, so my wish is to keep it intact. I said '*it*', but could be a male or female? For XRF PLOT see Page 40. 9

**CLOSE UP VIEW OF THE MYSTERIOUS STONE I FOUND ON ILKLEY MOOR DURING THE SUMMER, 1999. THIS PHOTOGRAPH IS: - 1 . 5 X THE ACTUAL SIZE.**

Gordon Holmes on the moor with his strange stone.

# Moor search leads to strange stone

**COURTESY OF THE ILKLEY GAZETTE FOR THEIR KIND PERMISSION, ALLOWING ME TO REPRODUCED THIS NEWS ARTICLE DATED: 1ˢᵗ July 1999.**

AMATEUR scientist and author Gordon Holmes thought he might have discovered an object from another planet when he found a strange stone on Ilkley Moor. Mr Holmes discovered the stone after combing the moors for meteorites.

He said: "I was looking at the Internet and got this idea that there might be more meteorites about than scientists were aware of.

"I spent about four weeks combing various moorlands at Baildon and Ilkley and about the fourth week I found this black strange looking object. It has all the characteristics of a meteorite. I have not found anything like it in the locality, it is pretty well unique."

Although the stone is unlikely to be a meteorite, as they are extremely rare, it has all the characteristics of one in appearance and density. Tests have shown it to have a high calcium level and low iron content, with magnetic properties, but it is thought to be an unusual stone up to 320 million years old, in comparison with other rocks in the locality around 150 to 180 million years old.

Mr Holmes has been inspired to write a book on the subject and will continue his search for an Ilkley Moor meteorite - if the stone had turned out to be the genuine article, it might have been worth around £5,000.

Mr Holmes said: "There is no doubt there are meteorites up there, the major problem is they look so much like terrestrial rocks."

10

# EVEN MORE MYSTERIES AT COTTINGLEY FAIRY WOODS.

The story of the Cottingley Fairies is world famous, however, there are still additional mysteries to be found at Cottingley's other wood. This is the wood I shall be describing; it is about a mile away from the famous one, at a place called; Blackhills. Which just happens to be the Bradford Scout CampSite HQ.

I should know, I once camped there during a thunderstorm, everyone I know who has camped at Blackhills, have also experienced thunderstorms, strange!

During the late summer of '99', I was invited to join the 'Northern Earth Mysteries Group', on a search of the woods. Thanks especially to *John Billingsley, Valerie Shepherd and Marrion Madley.* They were keen for me to visit a Cup & Ring Stone, just recently discovered (by Val.), a few years ago and a number of circular indentations, found on the surface of several Millstone Grit Rocks. The woods are private and it is only because a member of the 'friends of the woods' escorted us, that we had been given permission to visit.

If there was ever a place that felt spooky, this was it. There is even a spectacular folly built on top of high cliffs near to these strange circular indentations. During Victorian Times, the Folly and Cliffs were visible from the opposite hillside of the Aire Valley, but due to tall trees, very little of it is now seen.

At this point in the plot, you may ask: - "where is the Meteorite connection here", please hang on, I am coming to it soon.

After noting and photographing a number of circular indentations of various diameters, some of which were obviously natural, whilst others appeared wo/manmade. No doubt, a few people may claim they are Alien-made, I certainly cannot prove otherwise, so it must be considered a possibility, although not by me. Virtually, the last set of indentations we visited, were several feet apart, split between two twenty foot high millstone rocks. Both indentations were about one metre diameter and half-hemispherically formed into their particular vertical cliff. There was a few metres difference up the slope between both opposing half hemispheres. One half sphere was above ground level, whilst the other was half buried in the ground.

A male member of the group just happened to mention, "both hemispheres may have been originally joined together", I froze on the spot. "*WHAT*", I exclaimed. In an instance, I realized the horrible potential of the fellows, comments.

If indeed his comments were correct, then this means something nearly perfectly spherical had formed in the rock, which millions of years ago was soft sand.

Using my one metre long wood stick, the vertical diameter was a few cent-metres smaller than across the horizontal plane. The extra mass of sand on top would explain this finding, but what could form a one-metre sphere in nature?

In the past, the odd Geologist has told me that this is a natural phenomena, but they have never fully described to me, how it can happen. For weeks after this shock find, I churned over idea after idea with no suitable solution. Then three weeks later it struck me, the idea that is, a spherical formed iron meteorite crashing into hard-baked sand may result in what has been found here. Eventually, the iron would rust away in time leaving a spherical void within the now hardened sandstone. The court is still out on this one.

**THANKS TO THE 'FRIENDS OF THE COTTINGLEY WOODS GROUP'.**
In the foreground, there is a mottled shape large rock, which resembles a meteorite but it is more than likely it was formed due to strange weathering processes. Nearly all the rocks found in this area belong to the millstone grit series. The property of this type of rock lends itself to be easily shaped by water erosion.
Across to the upper left, an archway is visible, part of the Ferrand's Folly. Most of the construction uses the millstone cliff for the foundations. During Victorian times this was a local hot-spot tourist attraction and would be visible across the Aire Valley, that is before the tall trees arrived.

# ENCOUNTERS OF THE COSMIC KIND.

According to the experts, there are about 19,000 meteorite falls on Earth each year. Most of these crash-land in Desert or Ocean areas. However, on average there is about five such objects found after being observed passing through the atmosphere, annually.

Since I began my recent exploration of Meteorites some 5 months ago, there has been one highly noted event, which joined the landmass of New Zealand. Typical of my luck, it is at the opposite side of the World from the UK. So there is no chance of a couple of hours down the motorway to look for fragments.

It may not be wise for me to suggest that it is unlucky not to be near to an impacting stone or metallic mass from Space. Especially, if the cosmic mass lands on any one. There is at least one confirmed death from such an encounter. The only recorded death, at present, from a meteorite, is an unfortunate dog.

If the stone had missed the dog, then it would not be too much of a surprise if it then decided to bury the Meteorite underground, to chew later! Imagine all those meteorite hunters spending hours looking for fragments. This dog certainly had the last laugh or every dog has it's day, sorry.

You are more likely to suffer several lightening strikes, before being hit by a meteorite. Pardon the pun; the laws are astronomical against death by a space rock, unless it is the Dooms Day Rock with name of the human race written across it.

One rock 4km wide is believed to have wiped out the Dinosaurs, 65 million years ago. In fact, about 65% of all life died, during that period as a result of the impact and the aftermath. It is possible that several new geological ages have either began or ended due to these extra-terrestrial ping pong invaders.

If the Moon's cratered surface is anything to go by, then this local part of the Solar System must have been very active in the Earth's early history. It was thanks to the Solar System's early planet building processes that we (life forms) came into existence. What an irony it would be, if a delay in the process should wipe out that very life, it first created. Please note there is no intention to rule out any ones religion here, this is purely from a scientific point of view.

It seems that even Meteorites work to rules. There is a near perfect mathematical relationship between the mass of a Meteorite (or size) and the frequencies at which they crash land on Earth. That is fortunate in a way, since the big dangerous ones, only visit Earth about every 100,000 years or so. Whilst, microscopic meteorite dust, frequently rains down across the earth's entire surface. This mathematical relationship is not derived by a straight-line law but is based upon an exponential curve. Basically, what this means is those massive masses, which are capable of changing Geological Ages, are very rare these days. According to Planetary Scientists, several bombardment periods have occurred in the history of the Solar System. Most of this knowledge was formulated from the impact counts seen on Mercury, Mars, the moons of planets including our own Moon and even the Earth. As expected, the most active period for Meteorites happened during the formation of the Solar System. It is thanks to the early space probes of the 1960s and 1970s that provided much of this chronological information.

Plots number of Meteorites to be expected against the hours in a day. According to several sources, late afternoon is the time when the most meteorites are expected. However, during summer months (maximum daylight) cannot be the best for observation.

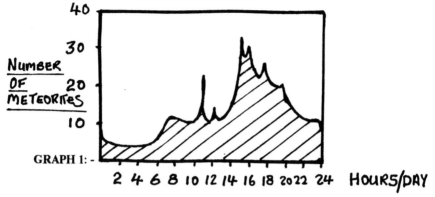

GRAPH 1: -

**WHAT IS THE BEST TIME TO OBSERVE METEORITES?**

The most obvious answer to this question would be to say, during a Meteorite Shower. However, this would not be exactly correct. The number of meteorites observed during a shower can vary dramatically; often a single highly rated shower event can turn out to be a poor display. The time for the maximum number of Meteorites expected can often suffer from a deviation of several hours and even the days. Predicting a good shower is a method less accurate than that of predicting the weather forecast.

There are however, some theoretical patterns that provide some general guidance to the nominal expected rates of Meteorite Falls observed. Based upon the two graphs provided: -

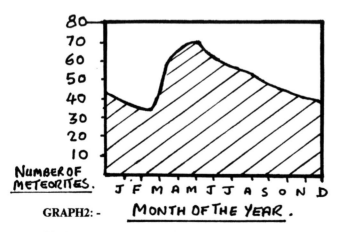

GRAPH2: -

Displays the expected number of Meteorites per month during the year expected. The months of May and June appear to be the prime months, but once again due to the increased daylight, not best for observation.

## MORE DETAILS ABOUT METEORITES.

My first visit to Oxford was during the teenage years. I was lucky enough to have been taken on a tour of the Natural History Museum there. A very vivid moment was when I spotted the collection of Meteorites on display. One metallic specimen had a distinct pattern covering the entire outer surface of the piece. Without hesitation, I remarked, "that looks like some sort of life-form", not far away, another visitor looked slightly startled by my remarks (this was about 1965). To this day, I have often wondered if that other person was the well-known Astronomer, Sir Fred Hoyle. The technical term for the pattern I am describing is Widmanstatten, whose presence depends upon the bulk Nickel content relative to the Iron Meteorite. In most circumstances, a Meteorite with a high Nickel content is adequate proof of the space origins of that item. Since Earth-based minerals, do not contain such high levels of Nickel naturally.

On my way home from work around the winter of 1971, I saw a huge purple fireball in the West, nearly horizontally in the distance. Although the actual dimensions of the presumed solid falling object, may have been less than pea size. The important point to note here is the colour of the Fireball. Metallurgists and Chemists know only to well what elements give off certain colour glows.

This Photograph showing a Collection of Meteorites and the one shown at the top of Page 37, are Dedicated to David Baker, who died during September 1999. Published here, thanks to the kind permission of his father.

The inspiration of David and the Layout of his Collection at the Ilkley Fossil & Gem Fair during March 1999 eventually led me to the Publication of this book.

When buying Meteorites, it is better to use the Main Dealers, as described here, to avoid forgeries. They will often Certify their products for their Customers.

# 2,000 BC - ANCIENT MILLENNIUM CALENDARS ON ILKLEY MOOR!

During the summer of 1999, whilst searching Ilkley Moor, rather optimistically looking for Meteorites, I noticed a very unusual astronomical event. This was just after arriving at one of the three stone circles that exist on Ilkley Moor. This ancient site is called *'Grub Stones - Stone Circle'*. Whilst standing there at the centre of these 4,000 year old prehistoric stones, I noticed that the Sun was setting on the horizon and the Full Moon had just recently risen above the ground, nearly directly opposite in the sky.

Based on my knowledge of Astronomy, I realized that returning to this site again the following evening, one should witness a near perfect alignment between the Sun, Moon, two outer standing stones and a central fallen stone consisting of an inverted rifle-like-sight.

Armed with a Camera, this rare mystic-like event was recorded on the evening of the 27th July 1999. The next few days, were spent calculating for similar Astronomical Alignments for the year 1999. Using Astronomical Simulation Software to check my results, I concluded that such an event would happen for one day, every lunar month. This is obvious now, but it was not so at the time.

Another later discovery was, that one day every Lunar Year, another Stone Circle would also become aligned with the one at *'Grub Stones'*. The name of this other Stone Circle is the *'Apostle Stone Circle'*, since it now consists of twelve standing stones. Originally, this stone circle consisted of about twenty four stones.

What is startling about these discoveries is that there are only a few areas on the moor where such an event could be observed. It seems that I had stumbled across the reason why these Stone Circles were positioned at they're present location. If my assumptions are correct, then it means that these stone circles were used by prehistoric people as Ancient Calendars set in stone. It seems their purpose was to determine such events as the planting season and harvest time. In other words, they could be referred to as Ancient Millenium Calendars used over 4,000 years ago.

My two previous published books regarding stone carvings found on Baildon Moor, shows a strong correlation between the rock art and certain well known Star Constellations. It is over fifteen years ago since my first discovery, of a potential Solstice Alignment site on the southwest side of Ilkley Moor, at Rivock Edge near Keighley.

**SOLSTICE ALIGNMENT SITE AT RIVOCK EDGE**

GTH © 1997

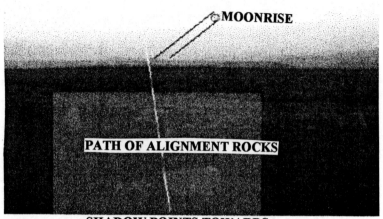

MOONRISE

PATH OF ALIGNMENT ROCKS

SHADOW POINTS TOWARDS MOONRISE

PHOTOGRAPHS OF MY DISCOVERY OF THE ASTRONOMY / STONE CIRCLE ALIGNMENTS.

COMPASS SAT ON TOP OF ALIGNMENT ROCK.

**Milky Way.**

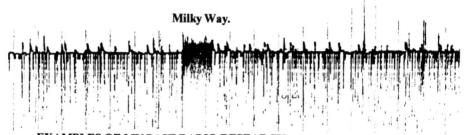

## EXAMPLES OF MY PAST RADIO RESEARCH.

During a Saturday class on Radio Astronomy and Satellite Tracking I ran at Hanson College Bradford, during the 1980s, I demonstrated what could be achieved with basic radio equipment. Using a home-made 137 MHz Yagi aerial connected to a simple electronic circuit for Integrating the radio signal and then connecting to a chart recorder. The central dark rectangular part of the graph represents one of the Spiral Arm of the Milky Way!
Exactly at the indicated position as shown on the Norton's Star Atlas.

This graph shows radio activity during one of the best August Meteorite Storms recorded in the last 20 years. Using a whip aerial supported by tent poles at a Camp Site near Eastbourne. The familiar 'PING' sounds were clearly heard.

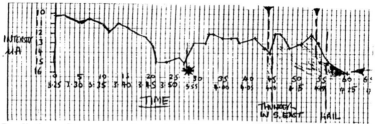

Predicting a Storm several minutes before it arrived is shown in this graph. The central star represents the precise time when I recorded the radio strength suddenly began to act erratically. Fifteen minutes later thunder was heard on the horizon, another ten minutes and it began to Hail violently. It was so bad, I had to move the equipment in-doors. This was the middle of Summer.
So this setup was a kind of Weather Radar.

## YOU CAN EVEN TUNE INTO METEORITES.

For those readers who want to do research or contribute to the Amateur Scientific Community, you can actually tune into Meteorites, indirectly. When a meteorite passes through the earth's atmosphere, it collides with atoms and knocks their electrons off. The air becomes ionized and the meteorite trail, which can be several kilometers long, acts like an aerial in the upper atmosphere. Now if the meteoroid trail is situated, say between the UK and Europe, it may act as a huge radio signal reflector in the sky. If a radio station in Poland is transmitting, the chances are due to the curvature of the earth, that we in Britain, will not be able to receive this signal.

For the sake of the above statement, I am ignoring unusual weather conditions, solar maximums and the Ionosphere.

What happens is that normally we are unable to hear this Polish Radio Station, however, if a meteorite trail forms in the ideal position, for several seconds the signal is reflected on towards the UK. This type of phenomena is often referred to as Meteor Scatter and/or Forward Scatter of Meteorites. Now if we tune into a suitable frequency, normally we will not hear anything, until a Meteor enters the Atmosphere at just the right trajectory. Contact may last typically up to forty seconds approximately. If instead of listening to the signal, it is connected to a chart recorder, then you may obtain an increase in signal strength represented by a positive peak on the chart.

Generally, suitable frequencies for this type of research are 70.31 MHz [Gdansk] and 66.62 MHz [Budapest]. In order to obtain the most efficient signal intensity, you must use the correct type of aerial with your radio or radio scanner. The old Band 1, 'H' shaped aerials for BBC1 are ideal, if you can get hold of one that is.

NOTE: if you are not familiar in such matters, before parting with any money, effort or from a SAFETY point of view, it is best to contact a Radio Amateur or Radio Engineer for help first. For those persons who enjoy the easy life, you could download the radio data from a *rf-* scanner to a RF-Shielded Computer, again contact the experts for advise.

Meteorite Showers, although not always, are a good time to tune into our distant European Radio Stations, in the hope that a short burst of perhaps Polish music or language is heard.

Meteor Scatter 'MS', is a specialized hobby that can take years for one to become fully experienced in, due to the sometimes-unpredictable conditions within the atmosphere. However, the satisfaction is the power of pure research and the ability to understand your results, accurately. In terms of population, not many people are doing it! Which leads me into one of those Club Car Sticker banners: 'Meteor Scatter Folk, do it from above'!

An example of my quick basic software
showing how radio signals are effected
during the period of a Partial Eclipse.

# SO YOU THINK YOU HAVE FOUND A METEORITE.

If you think you have found a Meteorite don't panic. Unfortunately, the chances are, certainly in this country, not very high. Does it appear to have a dark crust, unlike other rocks in the area? Is the mass of the stone at least three times as heavy as other rocks locally? Does it deflect a compass needle when it is past over it? Any signs of Ablations, which are shallow-like concave dimples, found across the outer surface. At this point, if you said yes to the all the previous questions then the odds against it being a Meteorite are beginning to tumble. Slag sometimes has a similar appearance to Meteorites, but the blowholes often give the game away? Although various sizes of holes are common on the real thing. Is there any signs of an impact. Ideally, at this stage you will now photograph the object from several different positions. Make a written note of the exact position, time and date it was found. You will be wearing those free plastic gloves that can be obtained from certain petrol stations. Next, you transfer the item into a previous, unused plastic bag. This is assuming it is not bigger than a football. No attempt should be made to lift it, if it lies in an awkward position, it has sharp edges or it is heavy. Only lift, using the correct techniques involved, do not lift with a bent back, always get help.

Until it is proved not to be the genuine article, it is best not to handle it at all without a layer of virgin plastic in-between you and the stone from the blue.

After thousands of years of impacts, you would think we would be tripping over the stuff and perhaps we are. Cosmic matter may exist all over the landscape just like on the Moon. Unfortunately, our Earth's geology has been active in the past.

The main problem is space stones begin to resemble terrestrial rocks and the Iron Meteorites, rust. Any signs of fossils then, forget any thoughts of appearing in the local press, unless you just happened to have found the first signs of life from another part of the Solar System or Galaxy!

Even if it appears non-magnetic, do not assume the worst, because some specimens have weak magnetic strength that will not deflect the compass needle. The overall shape may also help you determine if it is possible, it has past through the Earth's Atmosphere. If you have had plenty of time and resources to research Meteorites before the expedition, you may be able to compare this potential extra-terrestrial against photographs or technical descriptions.

When searching a beach, avoid being cut off by the tide. Likewise if you are high up avoid falling, or look out for objects above you, ready to come crashing down. In other words do not concentrate too much on the search; be aware of your circumstances. Avoid bad weather, lonely sites, bulls in fields, the list just grows.

One unusual experience is, if your mind begins to wander, keep a track of time and do not over do it. Every one needs a rest, of course. Did you bring a pal, food, map & compass, drinks, first-aid equipment with you, plus the charged-up Mobile?

Please note - this is NOT a complete list, but I do not want to bore you any more.

Good Hunting, if you do find a Meteorite or Tektite, any chance of a 5% cut?

## DISCLAIMER:

THE NOVEL: - 'MERLIN'S METEORITE', is complete fiction, the Names chosen are not a reference to any living person and thus it is not an infringement. Any similarities to a known person are therefore, a coincidence.

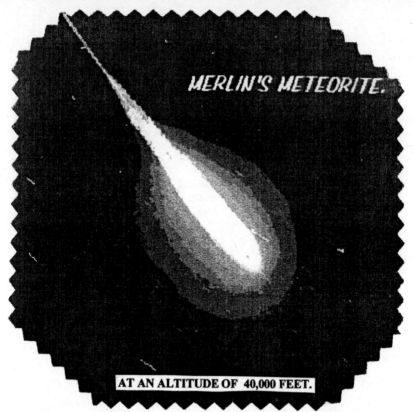

**MERLIN'S METEORITE.**

**AT AN ALTITUDE OF 40,000 FEET.**

In this Story, a long distant relation to Mother Shipton is born at a Farm Cottage on Ilkley Moor. Locally, Mother Shipton is well known for having the ability to predict the future. It is said she once claimed 'that iron would float' and apart from a bit of added Carbon and a few other Elements, she had correctly anticipated, the Steel Hull of a Ship. It seems the young child of the moor, would also have the ability of prediction, hence, he acquired the nickname of **MERLIN**.

Now Ilkley is a quiet little, beautiful town on the edge of the Moors and situated along the valley of Wharfedale. On some days and Sundays, you would probably hear more noise coming from a Glacier in Antarctica on a Wednesday than from the Avenues of Ilkley. That is not to say the place is like a Ghost Town, far from it, the reason things are quiet is, people enjoy living there.

However, Ilkley's peace is about to be shattered due to another piece, a big chunk of Rock from Space. The story consists of a series of extracts that describe various events due to this interference from above.

You are invited to join the gaps together through your own imagination; there are no limits to the variations possible.

With a bit of Luck, one day a Friendly Meteorite will crash-land on the moor and someone will send me a small sample to cherish.

My next wish is for a Rich Film Producer to transfer my book into a Big Film, in a similar mould to another locally famous phenomena, the Mystical *'Fairies of Cottingley Woods'*.

*If we wish upon a Star and not a Meteorite, our dream may come true!* 21

**MERLIN.** His real name was Allan M. Gray; he had lived on the moors for most of his life. In fact, he was born at *'Heather Cottage'* in 1917, the son of a Sheep Farmer. During those years between the World Wars, there was three cottages grouped into a single hamlet, the only local industry capable of surviving on this harsh northern expanse, was Sheep Farming. Even when a child, Allan began to be looked upon by his neighbors for having unusual powers. When he was seven years old playing with friends near the White Stones area, he suddenly urged them to take cover behind a large boulder. No sooner had they dived behind the rock when a bolt of lightening struck the ground where they had been standing. On return to school the next day, his best friend Elizabeth told the class he had powers of magic. When the old Science teacher, Walter Holborn, who the class named 'Whally Holly', heard the story, he nicknamed the Gray Lad, *Merlin*. We believe he got the idea from the lad's middle Initial, however, we never did know what the 'M' stood for. The name 'Merlin', became the kids new name, even his parents eventually would use the name when not concentrating.

Another rumor circulating around, during those early school days, was that the redheaded kid was a distant relation to Mother Shipton, a well-known prophet. Again, the claim was never proven although, in later life, many people experienced his pain reduction healing powers. Using the cold moorland spring water, sprinkled over the affected area often seemed to relief the pain nearly immediately. However, according to the odd critic it was the cold numbing affect that really achieved the result. For most of his life, Merlin would have a following of believers that swore by his cures and prophecies. As it turned out, this famous prophecy would prove to be the most accurate one he would ever make. To this day, it is claimed, the only way he could have known the truth before the event would be, if he had been a Russian Spy. Since he was in his late Seventies when he spoke this prediction, no one really believes that.   **MERLIN'S PROPHECY**

*ONE DAY SOON, A FIERY DRAGON  WILL SPIT UPON THE LAND OF WHARFEDALE.  WHERE A BALLARD WAS MADE FAMOUS AND THE WHITE WELL IS TO BE FOUND. THE CALF IS SEPARATE FROM HER OWN; ALSO WHERE ROMANS WERE FREE AND OLD.*
*AVOID THE BADGER AND ROCK ART, KEEP THE SWASTIKA APART. WHEN THE SKY DRAWS BLACK BLOODS ON CORNWALL'S STONE CIRCLES, THEN NOT LONG AFTER, YOU WILL SEE A FRIGHT UPON THE APOSTLE'S SIGHT. ON THAT VERY NIGHT, THE HEATHER WILL REMAIN BRIGHT, UNTIL THE DAWNING LIGHT.*
*THREE TREE RINGS WILL GROW, ALTHOUGH THERE WILL BE MERRYMENT AND SNOW.*
*A BLACK GLASS WILL FALL TO EARTH WITNESSED BY ONE AND ALL, BEWARE OF THE GLAZE FOR THE STORY BEGINS WITH HASTE.*

There was no doubt in Gordo's mind; the Prophecy was describing the moors about Ilkley. The encounter would take place near to the Apostle Stone Circle on route via 'The Cow & Calf Rocks', avoiding the slumbering figure of the Badger Stone covered with Cup & Ring patterns, similar to those found across the moors.

Within the rhyme it states 'the sky draws black blood on Cornwall', must be describing the 1999 Eclipse, then, 'three tree rings will grow', puts the event at the Winter of 2,002AD. The 'merry snow' suggests around the Christmas period. No one in the group including Gordo could explain the last verse, although Black Glass seems to be describing a special kind of Meteorite.

**PC Philip Blobbs read out the police document regarding the *Ilkley Mafia*:-**

*The Ilkley Mafia is a real roughneck group of criminal misfits that you would never want to meet. Consisting of bullies, muggers, violent so-called football supporters, whose leader or GodFather is Jake (Big&Mean) Kitson. His criminal record is that bad, it would relegate Ned Kelly to a Saint-like person!*

Membership of this notorious group stood at eleven, with two previous members banned, one for helping an old lady across the road and the other for returning stolen goods to their rightful owner by mistake.

According to the local press, the group's motto was, 'not only steal from the rich, but while you are at it, grab a loaf from the poor'.

It was 1997 when the Ilkley Mafia hit the local headlines, for the raid on the safe at the 'New Mums To Be Shop'. The event was a disaster for the group's reputation, for instead of grabbing the 20,000 Pounds Salaries payroll, they ended up with five dozen pairs of Non-Wet Nappies.

Seven very quite months passed before anyone heard news from the gang that year. The joke in town was, the group's motto must be 'we nick everything from the Top to the BOTTOM'.

Jake received news of the impact prophecy via the gang's infamous grape-vine known as Josh 'the Posh' Cooper, who had threaten to torture one of the 22nd Ilkley Scouts by rubbing itching cream on the back of his neck. The poor lad confessed everything he knew before escaping, due to Josh falling 3metres down a lift-shaft in the dark. When the fire brigade arrived on the scene, they refused to let him out of the shaft until he promised to return a 10metre ladder he had stolen from them, 6 months earlier.

The race was now on; five separate groups would compete to recover any Space Gems that were expected to crash-land soon onto the Moor.

**Photo-fit of Jake Kitson.**

# CONTACT WITH A UHFO. (UNIDENTIFIED HIGH FLYING OBJECT)

The Appleton Research Centre at Cambridge, Menwith Hill and Jodrell Bank had all known about, object UHFO 9870314 for the last three years.

It was estimated to be the size of a large pick-up wagon. No one in the West knew where this decaying satellite piece of Space Junk had originated from; however, it was not considered a threat to security. Based on the latest observations, it would enter Earth's orbit soon. Due to the highly eccentric orbital characteristics, it was not yet possible to predict where it would crash-land on Earth. The next couple of months would be crucial in determining the space boulder's final resting-place.

Radar contact had suggested it appears to be a large black-glass, loaf-shaped object. It only reflects about 30% of the radar signal; hence, it had been extremely difficult to monitor continuously.

65 DAYS LATER.

The Sky Eye Surveillance Computer Network - UK, has just confirmed the impact site at Ilkley Moor, about 5 km south of the Town. There was a sigh of relief from the MOD, it was feared the original Ground-Zero Site would be within the built up areas of either Bradford or Leeds in West Yorkshire. James Peterson, the Commander of SESCN-UK was now able to inform the Prime Minister of the meteorite's impact details. It would then be the decision of the Joint Cabinet Committee, just how and when the public would be told. According to the Top Secret Report from SESCN, that gave the Committee just eleven days notice. The Committee responded within 24 hours with the following report: -

CODENAMED: - 'AD' - AVOID DISASTER, FAX-0279657   17th December 2,002

The Committee made the following Recommendations:

1]    A circular security zone would extend from the point of Ground Zero by 3.5 km radius. No one would be allowed within this area. This is to occur immediately, as soon as all Wild Life was transported away to safety. Large sirens would sound four hours before impact, to scare off Birds and act as a warning to all.

2]    The Prime Minister would inform the public via the Six O'clock ŦBC1 News Programme on the evening of the 22nd December 2,002 AD.

3]    As a precautionary measure, persons wishing to evacuate the surrounding areas would be accommodated at Sport Centres and Church Halls within the Bradford and Leeds Districts. Transport Services would begin the task on the Evening of the 23rd December.

4]    Logistics and Security Operations would be the responsibility of the combined Military and Civilian Police Task Forces.

## MAP SHOWING EXPECTED IMPACT SITE.

↑N

COW & CALF ROCKS.

ILKLEY MOOR

APOSTLE STONE-CIRCLE

IMPACT SITE.

X

SECURITY ZONE

The Prime Minister has just announced to the IBC at 5:30pm GMT tonight, that", "*The Minister of Defense, Sir Michael Hesser OBE, has informed me that n five days time, a small Meteorite will crash-land upon the moorland near to Ikley in West Yorkshire". "There will be no danger to the public or buildings, owever, should people living within Ilkley or the surrounding areas desire, rovisions are to take affect regarding their safe evacuation 48 hours before the ime of impact".*

"Now over to our North of England Correspondent - Jill Jeffries".

"What is the latest Jill",

"Well here on the Edge of Ilkley Moor near to the beauty spot of the 'Cow and Calf Rocks', the Chief of Staff for the Cattrick Camp, Captain Anthony Bottomley, has told the IBC", "*The Meteorite is expected to produce a twenty foot diameter crater not far from the highest and most central remote part of the moorland, well away from any property". "The incoming missle..owh..arr..., sorry, Meteorite, should be visible across a thirty five mile radius from Ground Zero, which is where the object will hit the ground".*

"Is their any early signs of panic amongst the locals, Jill?

"Well no Rob, according to some local news reporter of the Ilkley Echo, a local man whose nickname is 'Merlin', made a prophecy about two months ago that the moors would be visited soon by an object from Space". "Apparently, the locals are more surprised by the media's late response, since the story was reported in the Ilkley Echo a few weeks ago".
"You do get this feeling Rob, the moors here have a sort of mystical appeal about them, also there are hundreds of so-called Cup and Rings Stones which are believed to be prehistoric rock carvings found at various sites across the Rombald Moors".
" Rombald Moors include the moorlands of Ilkley, Baildon, Otley, Rivock Edge near to Keighley and Skipton Moors". " In fact there is a local writer from Shipley who claims a few of the Cup and Ring Stones found on Baildon Moor represent Astronomical Phenomena".

"Quite fasinating Jill, what is that whining sound in the background, Jill ?

"That is the portable sirens Rob, it seems they are normally used in town centres to scare the Starlings from the buildings, however, they are having problems with them on the high moors, don't forget Rob these moorland are over 1,000 feet above sea-level, especially in the region the Meteorite is expected". :The Sirens are too light-weight, hence, they keep being blown over by the strong winds up here".
"Captain Bottomley has just informed me they are going to hold them down with sand bags, over to you Rob".

25

"Thanks Jill".

# MERLIN'S TREASURE HUNT FOR A REPLICA OF THE METEORITE.

## PLEASE READ THIS IMPORTANT NOTICE BEFORE AGREEING TO ATTEMPT MERLIN'S TREASURE HUNT.

DUE TO THE GENERAL VAGUENESS OF CLUES PROVIDED FOR DURING TREASURE HUNTS, THERE IS A HIGH PROBABILITY THAT PERSONS AND PETS MAY BECOME LOST ON THE MOOR. ALSO THE CHANCE OF INJURY IS INCREASED, THEREFORE, IF YOU INTEND TO PARTICPATE IN THIS TREASURE HUNT, YOU MUST TAKE FULL RESPONSIBILTY FOR YOURSELF AND/OR OTHER PERSONS AND CREATURES WHO ATTEND WITH YOU PLUS ANY DAMAGE OR LOSS OF MATERIALS / GOODS / TRANSPORT ETC.

YOU MUST BE FULLY PREPARED, TAKE: - O.S. MAP OF THE AREA & COMPASS, ADEQUATE AMOUNTS OF FOOD, A FULLY CHARGED MOBILE PHONE, WHISTLE, WATERPROOFS AND OTHER BRIGHT & COLOURFUL SUITABLE CLOTHING - IT MUST GIVE PROTECTION FROM THE SUN AND ADVERSE WEATHER. *DO NOT FORGET THIS PAGE OF CLUES.*

GO ONLY DURING DAYLIGHT HOURS, YOU MUST FINISH THE ATTEMPT, SEVERAL HOURS BEFORE SUNSET. AVOID FOG, STORMS, and BAD WEATHER. YOU AND OTHERS MUST BE OF EXCELLENT HEATH.

I, GORDON T. HOLMES DO NOT, OR MY FAMILY DOES NOT TAKE RESPONSIBILITY IN ANY WAY FOR THIS EVENT, OR FOR ANY INACCURATE OR WRONG INFORMATION GIVEN HERE, WHICH COULD LEAD TO ANY OR OTHER ABOVE DIFFICULTIES.

*UNLESS YOU KNOW THE AREA EXTREMELY WELL, YOU ARE ADVISED NOT TO ATTEMPT IT.* KEEP THIS PAGE IT IS FOR THE TREASURE HUNT ONLY.

Please complete the details below before proceeding with the Treasure Hunt.

Your full name:_____     Date _____

Witness: _____     Date _____

I agree to all the above rules, safety procedures and regulations.

The replica will be positioned ready to find from the 1<sup>st</sup> May 2,000 AD
until it is removed for the season on the 1<sup>st</sup> September 2,000 AD inclusive.

TREASURE HUNT CLUES TO FINDING THE REPLICA OF MERLIN'S METEORITE: -

From the Mother and her child above Ilkley, you proceed to find the stone ruin of Merlin's Cottage.
Search for the sleeper's path and when you reach the corner of the triangle, then walk through the stone gate of a circle.
Pass between the chosen stones with your back to the towers of technology.
Over the ridge you will find a grassy patch, stop there and seek Emley's line, passing carefully around the brook, head safely towards a distant knee-high rock, along her line.
Now turn with your left arm facing Thor's white circles; align with the iron box until you find a small triangular rock at 45 steps.
Still on that route, another three and digging deep you may find Merlin asleep.

Well Done, your first replica Meteorite find! If you find the glazed replica, please cover it over again, in the same position so that other people can also enjoy the pleasure of the Treasure Hunt. You may wish to leave a message in a plastic bag under it, so that we know how many people find it etc.

26

# THE WORLD'S PRESS IMPACTS ILKLEY!

As soon as the story leaked, news teams from around the World descended upon the town of Ilkley. Vans with Satellite dishes, giant floodlights everywhere and even a number of hired news helicopters crowding the skies. Ordinary folk in the street have nearly been forcefully dragged into portable cabins for interviews with well-known TV News Personalities. The whole atmosphere is alight, never in the history of this little sleepy hamlet of Whalfedale, as it experienced such sights.

Recent front page News Headlines referring to Ilkley, includes the following: -

| | |
|---|---|
| Doomsday Rock heading for Ilkley. | *Paris Press.* |
| "The Ilkley Moor Baht ' at Meteorite" | *Yorkshire Observer.* |
| Smack, Bang, Wallop, into Ilkley. | *Cardiff Headliner.* |
| UK - Moorland Meteorite Impact Soon. | *Washington Daily.* |
| Date: 27/12/2002 AD - Ground Zero, Ilkley. | *Glasgow Weekly.* |
| What's that there in the sky? Nowt much lad! | *London Press.* |
| Won't be long now, then we will know! | *Ilkley Echo.* |

A report in *'The Science News'* yesterday, claims the Ilkley Meteorite is in fact an Asteroid that originated from the Asteroid Field that orbits between the planets Mars and Jupiter. It may have begun the journey towards the inner solar system some five million years ago. It is believed to be over four billion years old, hence, one of the oldest members of our Solar System.
Dr David Hives said "These rocks are the original material from which the early proto-solar system formed about 4.6 Billion years ago". "Mars, Earth, Venus and Mercury would have formed due to countless boulders, the size of houses, smashing into one another over thousands of years, eventually forming the inner planets". "This would not be the case for the outer planets such as Jupiter, Saturn, Uranus and Neptune, which consist mainly of Gases". "The principle of the outer planet formation, called *gaseous accretion*, is still not fully understood".

The Geologist Weekly Newspaper, *'British Rocks'*, warns that there will be a *flood of gold-diggers*, searching the moors for specimens. Meteorites, especially English ones, will command high prices by collectors due to their rarity. It will not be a surprise to most people to learn that the country with the greatest number of collectors is the United States.
Over there, they have the biggest, the brightest rocks on the planet, not forgetting the number one all time great, Meteorite Crater, Arizona.
When you consider that a fragment the size of a child's marble can expect to pull prices of 15 Pounds or more, you realize that anyone wanting to make a quick buck will be heading Ilkley Bound. Trying to stop an invading army of meteorite magpies will be an impossible task on behalf of the authorities.
No doubt, a few will be willing to put their lives on the line, in order to be the first to obtain the rich pickings.

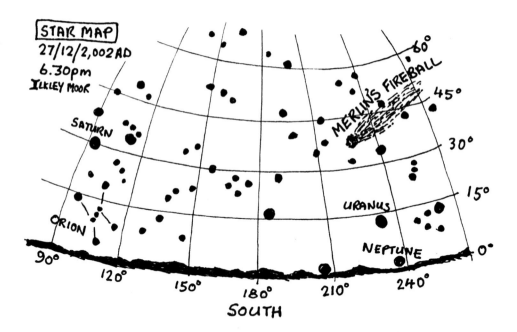

**STAR MAP**
27/12/2,002 AD
6.30pm
ILKLEY MOOR

SATURN

MERLIN'S FIREBALL

ORION

URANUS

NEPTUNE

60°
45°
30°
15°
0°

90°
120°
150°
180°
210°
240°

SOUTH

## MERLIN'S FIREBALL OBSERVED FROM THE APOSTLE STONE CIRCLE.

Using his night-vision camera, Gordo reproduced this sketch based on the
original photograph. The appearance of shadows next to the stones is due to a
floodlight been positioned to the right and off the page. Due to the high
magnification lens used, the fireball appears beyond the stone circle but it is in
fact, in front of the stones.

*Merlin's Meteorite from
The Apostle Stone Circle.*

28
Gordon T. Holmes ©

Generally, when we need an answer to a problem of today or in the future, one solution is to go back in time and research the historical record. Thanks to the power of the Internet and the resources of Bradford University, I have provided a brief historical record of several major fireballs witnessed over the British Isles: -

On the 11th December 1741, a fireball the size of the Moon, was seen travelling from the West to the East over the Isle of Wight.

A fireball on the 18th August 1783 was seen first in the Shetland Isles, past over York where it was heard to explode and continued on to Burgundy in France. A journey of 1200 miles, at Greenwich it consisted of a brilliant double bolide.

Some fireballs have been so bright that they are compared to daylight. For instance the one of 25th November 1758, passing near Edinburgh and Dublin. Another fireball passing London on the 2nd December 1814.

Fireballs not only produce light but also sound, in 1872 at Nairn, Scotland a sound compared to three or four cannons was heard. The 1873, Liverpool and Chester fireball sounded as loud as a roll of thunder and the 1874 Holyhead, Wales fireball, made crackling sounds.

The list above is far from complete for the period of years stated but provides the impression of the observed power of fireballs. These examples were only classed as small ones, imagine the destruction possible due to a large object.

A once in a lifetime event occurred during the second week of July 1994, when the twenty plus fragments from the Comet: - Shoemaker-Levy 9, smashed into the upper atmosphere of Jupiter. Some pieces were 4km across and produced explosions as large as the Earth. Using basic radio equipment, electronic circuits and a second-hand medical chart recorder I managed to obtain several radio bursts of the spectacular event. (refer to: - "Radio Observations of Shoemaker-Levy 9 Comet", SASRG PRESS, Gordon T. Holmes). This example shown below was the most impressive of my collection.

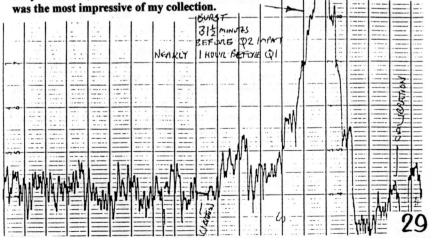

## METEORITE MADNESS AT ILKLEY.

Ilkley is booming, since the news broke of the future impending encounter of the extraterrestrial type. Tourism has increased by three to four times the normal expected, for the Christmas festive season. Sales of CD-Players, Sports Cars and even Cuddly Toys were virtually sold-out; "it seems customers are living today in case there is no tomorrow". said a local trader.

The Police report a crime-wave involving the stealing of street signs and according to some traders, signs with the name 'Ilkley' are fetching as much as one thousand pounds on the black market. It did not take local business that long to cotton on to the idea, for they are now selling plastic replica signs for only one hundredth the cost of the recent going rate for the genuine item.

You can even buy plastic models of houses with holes in the roof, which were supposed to have been produced by a few meteorites.

Next years 'Ilkley Tourist Guide' is on hold at the publishers, with the present modified opening passage: -

*Ilkley, famous for a ballad regarding the local moorland, the home of Romans, the Cow & Calf Rocks, a White Well and an encounter with a Meteorite in 2,002AD. Come and visit the original crater - - - - - - - - - - - [ details as and when available] now a protected site!*

For one day last week, more people were visiting Ilkley than were visiting the Disney Theme Park at Parkhead. Schools in the area broke up one week earlier than usual for Christmas, to provide time for families planning trips away from the district until any possible threat from the sky, is over. Travel Agents have reported a 20% increase in holidays to Europe. Even Patrick Moore's next *Sky at Night Programme*, is to be screened live from Ilkley, during impact night.

The only anti-climax is the decision by the Churches not to ring the bells-in for Christmas, until any potential danger is passed. Most locals and the Council agreed fully with the Churches decision, no one wants to temp providence.

So this little quiet beautiful town of Ilkley, set on the northern slopes of the moorland, may never be the same again. Forever, to be part of the early 21$^{st}$ Century folklore, the first place in Europe to be visited by a Meteorite in the new century. Finally, during the two festive weeks, house prices actually fell by an estimated 15% since homeowners feared the worst. Compared with the other commodities, this was the only unusual product price reversal, which quickly recovered after the 27$^{th}$.

One long-term affect based on the influence of all this publicity, was good news for the Universities. There was a remarkable increase in the student population, especially, for the Science related Courses at Bradford, Leeds, York, Sheffield and Hull. The previous lowly attendance levels of students applying for the specialized Space and Planetary Science degree subjects had a dramatic turnaround in their fortunes, thanks to the impacting visitor from Space. Even nationwide, there was an estimated increase of 8% more science students as a directly result of the Ilkley episode.

30

## IMPACT - GROUND ZERO.

Various local groups began to assembly along the temporary installed perimeter fence. The UFO Group had positioned themselves at three locations, each 120 degrees apart. This was just in case the crash-landing site was difficult to locate; then they could use triangulation methods to pin point the impact area precisely. At each station, the group had set up 20 X 50 binoculars on stands.
Ilkley's Astronomy Group and the Buddhists had clustered together on the Ilkley side, looking towards the Southwest, hoping to obtain the best observation vantage-point of the incoming fireball. The Ilkley Mafia had just appeared on the scene, no doubt up to no good. With only 30 minutes to go before the expected fireball display, the patrolled fence was only lightly manned. Apparently a police transport bus, with 60 officers on board, had broken down on the steep hill near to the Cow & Calf rocks. According to voice communications, they were walking the last 1.5 miles on foot. Altogether, there was about sixty on-lookers and just seven police or military personnel guarding the fence.

## CONTACT IS MADE.        [ Julian Day 2452636, Moon 22.62 days old ]

It was Group B, part of the UFO people who first saw the incoming flames of the fireball, thanks to their binocular on stand. "Yes, it is there, my gosh, I can see an intense white blinding glow surrounded by a blue haze", said one of the group members. Everyone cheered and began to dance about on the spot. Suddenly, the Ilkley Mafia made a dash for it, using a blank of wood, they quickly clambered over the four-foot high fence. Panic broke out, has a couple of officers set off in pursuit, chasing the gang over the moors. Within an instance, several other people decided to scale the comical security measure and head off in the direction of where the Fireball looked to be heading.

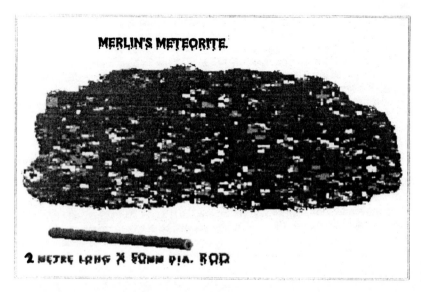

MERLIN'S METEORITE.

2 METRE LONG X 50mm DIA. ROD

31

The TV cameras were all pointing skywards, even the *'The Sky at Night'* team had setup to record the event with what looked like Patrick Moore heavily clothed, pointing upwards. One of the Astronomy group members shouted out, "it is coming in at an angle of 37 degrees, Gee I can see it spitting out purple, red white and blue matter in all directions".

In the distance just over the next plateau (*plateaux* or moorland shelve), at about 1200 ft above sea level, an impact glow burst into view over the brow of the hill. A few seconds later, two Supersonic Booms were heard miles away. We found out later that the meteorite had been seen over forty-five miles away. It had been seen from as far as Doncaster, York, Skipton and even Huddersfield.

Jake was only 200 yards from the point of impact, when a multitude of pieces recoiled upwards into the air. Although, it was the gang's intention to grab as many pieces as possible, to sell to collectors on the black-market. Jake would acquire a specimen easier than he originally hoped for, since one golf-ball size chunk landed directly on his head. Fortunately, his woolly hat dampened most of the blow, has he fell stunned on to the heather. Two First -Aid attendants arrived, put him on a stretcher, and then went off searching for bits of meteorite. With Jake groaning in agony, a police officer went over to help. In an amazing burst of energy, Jake got to his feet and made off in the distance with the rest of the gang following close behind. That was the last time the Ilkley Mafia was ever seen, rumor has it, they vanished over the border to Lancashire.

Weeks before, most of the major Newspapers had offered financial rewards to anyone, for 'bits of the meteorite'. So everyone, including certain uniformed personnel, were busily collecting chunk loads of black glazed material. Although it was nighttime, thanks to the surface covering of snow, it was easy to spot pieces upon the ground. The Ilkley Scout Group arrived with an enormous cart; several people were offering them money for hire of space on the cart, to carry their heavy booty. It was for all the world, a scene out of the pages of the *'Gold-Diggers of the Wild West'*. "A lot of people, made a lot of money that night", claimed one of the daily tabloids, the next day.

## THE VISION OF MERLIN.

At first light, of the sixty odd people on the moor last night, the numbers had dwindled down to fifteen. After hours of searching, no one had found the main fireball, only hundreds of small shattered black glazed lumps. Due to the low angle of atmospheric entry, it seems the loaf shaped object had bounced a few times and probably disappeared down into one of the nearby gullies. We all headed for the Apostle Stone Circle with the intention of calling of the search, when in the distance a strange number of figures appeared silhouetted by the Sunrise. As they approached, we could here them shouting. Curious to investigate, we all set off in the direction of this morning vision. It was one of the scouts, who first identify the spooky shapes. "Good Grief, Merlin, it is Mr. Gray sat on our scout cart being pulled by four blokes". He was pointing over the ridge opposite. A few of us scrambled over to where he had indicated. Merlin was in his 80s now, frail with long Grey hair. When we reached the edge of the ridge, we all stood, stunned into silence. There it was at last, half buried in the snow and mud, the rock from Space. That same scout shouted out, "it is Merlin's Meteorite", we all nodded in agreement. At that moment, old Gray gave a wave and then was driven off at speed, back in the direction of the sunrise. Yes, during that morning, we had indeed seen the Vision of Merlin!

# THE STONE IS EXAMINED.

Two weeks after the impact near Ilkley, the car-size Stone finally arrives at the Zen Laboratories in Oxford. The most powerful laser in the UK would attempt to penetrate the black glassy surface and discover what secrets are found within. Eight representatives had been invited to the Examination to observe and report the scientific findings to their particular groups.

It was about 11am when the laser test firing was ready; a blast of 60megavolts force for only sixteen nanoseconds should be enough to obtain a complete material signature.

As observers we all sat behind armor-glass, as we waited, the countdown began, "TEST ALPHA, begin: - 10 - 9 - 8 -7 - 6 - 5 - 4 - 3 - 2 - 1 zero", grrrroooowww.

A horrible screeching sound could be heard coming from the small plasma flame produced by the laser gun, Gordo had just uttered the word, "wow", when a gigantic boom occurred shaking the floor. Suddenly, there was panic inside the test chamber, as scientists and technicians were charging around the room in all directions or diving over tables or down onto the floor. After about twenty seconds, the haze from the explosion began to disperse due to the efficient extractor units. Red lights were flashing and alarms blaring out, it was so chaotic too watch, the eight of us all began laughing. It was just, for all the world, what you would expect to see in one of Peter Seller's Pink Panther films. Fortunately, the only thing that was hurt due to the blast was a few academic prides.

TWO HOURS LATER:

The scientists had recalculated the laser intensity and changed the frequency slightly. Then they decided to perform two firings, the initial one, would act as a pre-heat followed immediately by the main energetic beam. A bank of main-computers burst into life, processing the results. After a few minutes, the results in the form of multi-colour three-dimensional graphs were displayed on the large monitors, situated across the rooms. Excitement was growing, as people in white coats, were comparing their computerized chart-boards.

Then, a series of Alarms began clanging again; this time the sound was different to the previous episode. The Scientists starred at one another puzzled, suddenly the words: -

—— LIFE DETECTED —— LIFE DETECTED —— LIFE DETECTED ——

appeared across the screens.

This time, within the test-firing chamber, the scientist headed for the intermediate doors and once again in a state of panic. "Biological life should not have been detected within this Meteorite, no one had anticipated it", said a spokesperson.

Mainly based on the experiences of Nasa, after the Apollo Moon Landings, it was thought there was no life threatening microbes existing in any samples found in the solar system, except from Earth of course.

**24 HOURS AFTER LIFE WAS DETECTED: -**

When the news spilled out that life had been detected, there was an immediate News Blackout. The eight observers were told they would not be allowed to leave the laboratory building for at least the next 36 hours. That is until the Scientists decided the next possible action to take. We had to take an official oath of secrecy regarding the matter and it was made plain that we must not discuss what had been observed with anyone, until we were instructed otherwise. However, unknown to the security, staff and the rest of us, the group leader of the UFO team had secretly hidden a mobile phone to record and transfer the conversations during the meteorite examinations. Back in Ilkley, the rest of the UFO group had realised the significance of the events overheard from Zen. Before the hidden mobile had been uncovered by a sharp-eyed security chief, the momentous news had already been leaked to the press.
The next day's headlines included: -

*Bugs crawl out of Famous Ilkley Meteorite.*
*Fossils also detected within Moorland Space Rock.*
*Yorkshire and Oxford On-High, Alien Bugs Alert.*
*It came from Ilkley!*
*Cosmic Bugs found in Baht ' at.*

## SCIENTIFIC FINDINGS OF THE ZEN RESEARCH TEAM.

Prof. Trevor Restall had concluded that their scientific findings had indicated the so-called Ilkley Meteorite appeared to have been man-made. The process in the production of the outer black-glass coating was unknown in the West. Although the early results had indicated high levels of carbon, a new type of ceramic, limestone fossils and a small quantity of sea water plankton. Our results are presently inconclusive. Prof. Restall stated the following questions needed to be addressed before answers could be determined: -

1]      Who had created the Meteorite and how long had it been in Space?
2]      Was the same country as 1] responsible for launching it into Space?
3]      Why was a small quantity of life and fossils placed within the rock?
4]      What was the overall purpose of the experiment?

"Finally, since there is presently only a limited number of countries capable of launching a two ton mass object into Earth Orbit, why had there been no international consultation", stated Prof. Restall. "Our main concern is, was this an attempt to test a potential biological weapon-system, capable of delivering some horrible microbe menace to an unsuspecting country"?

Zen's Official Scientific Report Ended with the following paragraph: -

*The midnight lights would burn long and costly during the next few months in the West's Secret Service Departments. According to Pentagon, British and European Intelligence sources, there would be, pardon the pun, no stone left unturned, until we track down the creator and country of origin of the 'Ilkley Meteorite'.*

# THE RUSSIAN SPACE-STATION PROJECT: *'COALDUST'*.

It began with the defection of a top Russian Scientist in 1988, during the International Paris Trade Fair. After several weeks of intensive questioning, the following episode was revealed ( Pinocoff Vladskie had been involved with Project 'CoalDust', from the initial project aims, he describes in detail below what it was all about):-

In 1983 an experiment on board the Russian Space Station 'Mir', involved launching a large 2,100kg mass into a low re-entry orbit. The purpose was to see if a cosmic meteorite containing potential Alien living cells and fossils could survive a re-entry through the Earth's Atmosphere without being destroyed. This would indicate if life could have arrived on Earth from Space. Unfortunately, the Cosmonaut responsible for programming the Computer onboard *Mir* with the co-ordinates to allow the special cargo into a correct re-entry orbit, had accidentally typed in the wrong launch *prefix-code*. Instead of the manmade meteorite being destined to crash-land 200 km south of Moscow, it was instead booster into a highly elongated orbit which meant a unpredictable final resting place a few years into the future. The Russians had decided to keep the whole affair Secret, but due to the thaw in relations between the East & West after the Cold War, the details of the episode were passed over to the CIA, Nasa and MI6.
The wo/manmade Meteorite consisted of a single two tonne piece of coal from Siberia, which had been specially prepared to contain small compartments at the centre of the mass. A culture of single-cells and a flask of plakton was sealed within one compartment plus a separate container of fossil remains in another.
The Meteorite was then covered completely by a new type of Black Glazed Molten Ceramic produced in space using a cargo-ship furnace chamber. Earth-Based experiments had shown that a coating of only 25mm thickness would be sufficient for the object to survive the high temperature experience, when passing through the earth's atmosphere. This new ceramic resin was so strong and resilient that only a high-powered laser could penetrate through it. [ END OF REPORT ].

*EXTRACTS FROM THE 'MOD DIARY'    NOVEMBER 2,002AD:-*

3rd November 2,002AD.
Ms June Whitley, the MI6's field-agent for the West Yorksire region, who is assigned the task during December, of leaking the information to the local Yorks population to prepare them for the expected threat from Space.

7th November.
The Appleton Space Research Centre at Goonhilly Downs had calculated the impact would occur on the 27th December 2002, at 19:37 GMT. Somewhere in the region of Leeds or Bradford. *Suggestion:-* local population evacuated?
*Comments:* Usually, typical astronomical events are quoted in units of UT (Universal Time), but due to the possible lack of scientific terminology understood by the general public, it was felt converting the time to GMT (Greenwich Mean-Time) was far easier to relate to, rather than some Whiz-Kid's Astronomy time-base.

# THE AFTERMATH.

Two impacts had occurred upon Ilkley, one of them came from the sky, whilst the other had changed the way of life, in this past elegant Victorian town. Things began to slowly return to normal following the recent incredible events. Ilkley had experienced the most eventful Christmas Period in 4,000 years of his history. The World's Press had returned overseas and to a New Millennium, so there was much to keep it pre-occupied. This Gem in the Wharfedale Crown would never be the same. For years after the Meteorite incident, the Tourist Industry of Ilkley, just kept on growing. First-time visitors just wanted to see both Merlin's Crater and the town known as the Gateway to the Yorkshire Dales.

Thanks to the large bounty of money on offer, by a National Sunday Newspaper to persons or groups who could provide them with Video Footage, Photographic or physical evidence, certain parties stood to gain financially. Eventually, all the groups that captured some part of the Space related episode, decided to share their reward money equally.

The Scouts and UFO Group decided to half their resources in the form of a new hut HQ. IAG – the Ilkley Astronomy Group, bought a new 17" dia. Newtonian Reflector Telescope with Computer Control, so that kept the group busy for several years. That strange Religious Group, who never after all, experienced the end of the World, decided to look elsewhere for it. 'The Holy-One-Ones', booked a four-week holiday in Tibet and were never seen again. Rumour has it; the Yeti may have eaten them all.

Gordo had decided to return to his favourite hobby/past-time, that is scanning the Moors for Meteorites, Flint Tools, Cup & Ring Stones and anything else of interest. Should you happen to see him on the moor, ask him, how is old Merlin doing?

Never underestimate the strange mystic beauty and the gift of inner-spirit, when walking Rombald's Moors. Countless peoples of the past have lived here and have left ancient relics, most of which, is now lost. There is no doubt many examples of their way of life, must be still hidden just below the surface, ready to enlighten us at some future time.

Old Mr Gray died three years after the impact event. According to Merlin on his deathbed, if anyone harms the moors or tries to build on them, a great storm will arise and blow away the invaders. Certainly, the locals took heed and the council, for some years after, a new local land-act was created, where by no person or business, apart from a restricted Agriculture Farm, could be built within the moorland boundary.

The moor would remain forever protected, as long as Mankind remained, avoiding of course, any impacting destruction from Space.

In respect to Mr Gray (Merlin), the Ilkley Groups and Council denoted a slab fixed next to his tombstone, made from the Meteorite, with the words inscribed:-

*Here lies Allan (Merlin) Gray, who predicted the arrival of a heavenly stone, sent to Ilkley Moor, 27th December 2,002AD.*
*If you ever find yourself alone on the moor, when the wind blows softly, you may hear Merlin's voice.*
*Do not be afraid, for he is the Guardian of the Moor and nothing will harm you.*
*During the twilight of day, on the moors, if you listen closely you may hear the Skylark sing Merlin's Melody of Song.*

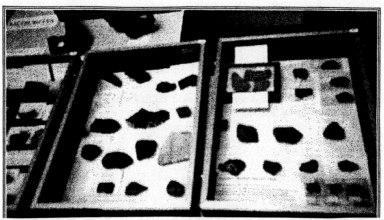

The largest piece shown here is just slightly larger than the average size of a computer mouse. You could expect to pay at least 200 pounds for specimens of this size. However, much depends on where the Meteorite was found, whether it is a stone, iron or a combination of both. As expected, the quality of the specimen can be critical. Meteorites with cracks or splits would be classed as poor examples although they do provide a stronger case for the genuine article. Once you become familiar with meteorites it would be difficult to be lumbered with a fake but the specified area it was found, 'could be wool over the eyes job'.

A COLLECTION OF METEORITES FOR SALE AT A LOCAL GEM SHOW.
[Reproduced thanks to the kind permission of David Baker]

The photograph shows a Tektite next to an old penny piece for scale. This Tektite is similar in appearance to Black Jet and is covered by many concave holes. Although it is hard, it is also brittle and comes from Thailand.
Tektites are only found at a few locations around the world. They come in shades of yellow, green, brown and black. The estimated value of this specimen is 20 pounds, generally Tektites are cheaper to buy than Meteorites.

# PHEW - THAT WAS A CLOSE SHAVE !    27/10/2028

Do you want the Good News or the Bad News?

Please can I have the Bad News First.

Yesterday, the Earth was wiped out at 6.31pm by a 1.3km wide Asteroid, named '1997XF11'. *This news was transmitted to the International Space Station from an automated robotic monitoring station on the lunar surface.*

What is the Good News?

**It happened on Thursday, so you will receive your latest salary slip hours before it arrives!**

This may sound a little far-fetched, but for a few hours just recently, the World's Press were claiming this story in their headlines. In fact, we may have to wait until the year 2,002AD, before the final orbit can be confirmed. So that it can be determined how close to the Earth the Asteroid will come, assuming it will miss!
Even before 2,028AD, we can expect about 15 Asteroids to pass close to the Earth. Fortunately, the Planet Jupiter protects us from the majority of Meteorite encounters. One recent famous example being the twenty plus fragments of the Comet: Shoemaker-Levy 9, which crashed in Jupiter during second week of July 1994. It is the Sun and Jupiter's large gravity affects, which diverts most space rocks away from the Earth and towards them. Recent evidence, in the last ten years, suggests large Meteorites are hitting the Earth at a higher frequency, than was previously thought.
According to some sources if Asteroid 1997 XF11 were to strike the Earth, it would produce a crater 20 miles across, tidal waves 100 feet high and probably wipe out a quarter of the World's Population. Yet this Asteroid, is only one-sixth the size of the one believed to have made the Dinosaurs extinct, 65 million years ago.
This threat from Space is far more serious than we previously were aware of. In fact, certain countries are now considering protection by early-warning radar and counter measures, such as using missiles to divert the Doomsday Rock.
One recent suggestion is, the Earth was hit by such a Doomsday object during the Middle Ages. There is very little recorded knowledge of this time, maybe due to mankind having to struggle just to survive the aftermath of a catastrophic explosion in, my guess China.
It makes you think though, the guys that go around with the banner, *'The end of the World is Nigh'*, *are* probably going to be right one day. Possibly, not all life will be destroyed; the humble Hamster could be the new dominant species! I wonder if this is a repeat of what happened 65 million years ago?

# CONCLUSIONS: IMPACTING NEW SCIENTIFIC THEORIES.

**It is rather strange that Meteorites may have seeded life on planets but eventually is destined to destroy that very same life, many eons later.  [G.T.H. Nov1999]**

Just when the scientific community have accepted that Dinosaurs were probably wiped out 65 million years ago by a Meteorite, then two scientists from Caltech, offer an alternative plausible theory. It seems that something nearly invisible, travelling at supersonic speeds and originated from many light years distance away, may have exterminated our Dino-monster friends.
The killers in question are known to Astronomers as Cosmic Rays; at certain periods in our past, these high-flying particles were pulverizing or cooking the brains of those ancient creatures. Something similar to standing in front of a microwave with the door open, hot stewed-brain, yak! Now our little lot, that is our very distant ancestors, were living down holes, not swinging about in the trees, Darwin! For the want of a name, please allow me to refer to these shrew-like creatures as *'homo-clawsicus'*.
The reason certain species survived was due to a number of factors and in some cases, pure luck. Scorpions survived because they were able to evolve resistance to higher levels of radiation from the intensive cosmic ray bombardment. *Homo-clawsicus* was not wiped out because the ground filtered out those harmful rays. Creatures that lived in swamps, crocs. and the like, fortunately had murky water for protection; in addition, lots of rotten flesh lying about.
Depending upon the rate of Cosmic Rays falling upon the Earth then, it may have taken anything from one year to thousands of years for the different species to adopt or die out.
There is no doubting the crater find in the Gulf of Mexico impacted 65,000,000 years ago, obviously was a Variable in the Extermination Formulae. Another Variable to consider was the intense volcanic activity, present at that time, causing one of the longest winters in history. Yet another deadly factor was due to high Solar Activity, the output received on Earth was both lethal and devastating.  If there was ever, an example of a Bad Time to be born this was it, the choice; cooking, frying, freezing and dying!
When the Apollo Astronauts went to the Moon, they experienced the occasional flash of light when their eyes were shut.  On examination of their Space Helmets and Suit, fine microscopic penetrating needles were found that had been produced by Cosmic Rays. Speaking from my own experiences, I have also experienced about two or three such events in recent years. The last one, just over one year ago; it was if someone had just flashed a light inside my optic nerve. The more we understand these external phenomena from Space, the more we realise their influence is far greater, than we were previously led to believe.
The study of Meteorites involves knowledge of many Sciences, these include: - Optical & Radio Astronomy, Astro & Particle Physics, Metallurgy, Statistics, Orbital Mechanics, Chemistry, History, Mechanics; the list just goes on and on. Therefore, if you decide to research the Science of Meteorites, you are really discovering a whole Spectrum of Sciences. There may not be that many examples to find on field trips, but there are many Museum pieces and the Internet Sites to search.
*Good Hunting: I hope you to will see and wish upon a Shooting Star.*

THE 'XRF' PLOT SHOWS A
HIGH CALCIUM CONTENT
AND SMALL AMOUNTS OF IRON.
THEREFORE, AS EXPECTED,
IT WAS SLIGHTLY MAGNETIC.

THANKS TO THE FACILITIES OF THE
DEPT. OF ARCHAEOLOGICAL SCIENCES,
BRADFORD UNIVERSITY AN D THE
EXPERTISE OF DR GERRY McDONNELL,
I WAS ABLE TO OBTAIN THIS 'XRF'-
PLOT OF THE ILKLEY STONE.

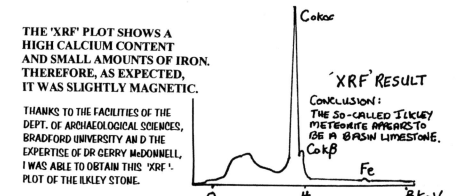

'XRF' RESULT

CONCLUSION:
THE SO-CALLED ILKLEY
METEORITE APPEARS TO
BE A BASIN LIMESTONE.

Certainly, in the last five years, the role of Meteorites in the overall scheme of Planet Forming, the Seeding of Life and the changes or glitches in Evolution is now better understood. With the renewed interest in Mars, it may not be long before life, or signs of life are detected there. We may soon arrive at that instance when 'Life is found beyond our Delicately Balanced World'.

Since arriving into the world, in the year 1952, I have witnessed: - Sputnik, Moon-Landings, Black Holes, Hubble Telescope, Seti and even the possibility that fossils have been found in a Martian Meteorite. These are indeed exciting times if you are interested in such matters. The Search for Life will continue, so will the Exploration of Space. We are near to making the Discoveries of where Mankind came from and finding the proof existence of other life forms. Apart from Complete- War or Destruction from a Heavenly Body, we are ready make that 'Giant Leap for all Mankind'!

J.F.Kennedy said, "We choose to go to the Moon", our next choice is many magnitudes greater than this, "We choose to go to the Stars"! In Time, the Technology will be found to make this dream come true. Instead of building a super spacecraft, the easier solution would be to hitch a ride on a Cool Comet (temperature about 100 degrees Centigrade). The inside of the Comet (at least 6km across) is furnished for a small colony of Space Explorers. It is their distant offspring (plus a DNA Variation Implant) who will arrive at a new solar system, with the technology to begin a New World. Were Adam and Eve, the offspring from a Historic Space Mission which arrived on Earth, in the past? Now that would be a good plot for my next book.

There are no shortages of potential stony spacecraft to be found at the Asteroid-Belt although, they need a big boost to start the venture. It is probably better to wait for the next passing Meteorite Shower or Comet. It is the stones, which travel far beyond the Solar System that, are required, for a trip to the Stars not the local No. 67s. Those who want the return journey type Meteorites, can always brag when they return home, that young Al was born inside a Meteorite. Now that would be a cosmic status symbol!

*Once Again, Good Meteorite Searching and/ or have a Safe Treasure Hunt.*